My Book About

Harry &
Meghan

How to Use this Book

Do you have something to say about Harry and Meghan?

Here's an opportunity to write your book about the younger son of Prince Charles and Princess Diana and his biracial, American-born wife.

This book includes a mix of lined and blank pages so you can write or draw. It's also illustrated with photos you can write captions for or just use for inspiration.

Not sure what to write? Check the next page for a list of ideas.

Fill in your name on the title page, add a dedication, then turn to page 13 and begin writing.

You can fill in the table of contents as you go or when you've finished.

Finally, if you would prefer that no one else sees these instructions, carefully remove this page from the book. We recommend using an exacto knife.

Now you're ready to proudly display *My Book About Harry & Meghan.*

Need some ideas to help you get started?
Write your thoughts on:

• Harry's childhood—growing up in the royal family and losing his mother at a young age.

• Harry's work with charities, particularly the Invictus Games.

• Meghan's career as an actor.

• Meghan's relationship with her family.

• Why so many Americans are fascinated by British royalty.

• Harry and Meghan's business deals since they resigned from their royal duties.

• The multifaceted issue of race, Harry and Meghan, and the royal family.

• The interview Harry and Meghan did with Oprah Winfrey.

• How Harry and Meghan behave with one another in public.

• Harry and Meghan's relationship with the royal family.

• The attention Harry and Meghan have gotten from the press.

• Harry and Meghan's political and social views.

• How Harry and Meghan inspire you.

My Book About

Harry &
Meghan

By

_____

Dedication

_____

_____

_____

_____

_____

_____

_____

_____

_____

_____

Contents

Photo: © Gunter Hofer | Dreamstime.com

_____
_____
_____
_____
_____
_____
_____
_____
_____
_____
_____
_____
_____
_____
_____
_____
_____
_____
_____

_____

_____

_____

_____

_____

_____

_____

_____

_____

_____

_____

_____

_____

_____

_____

_____

_____

_____

_____

_____

_____

_____

_____

_____

_____

_____

_____

_____

_____

_____

_____

_____

_____

_____

_____

_____

_____

_____

_____

_____

_____

_____

Photo: © Andrew Bartlett | Dreamstime.com

_____

_____

_____

_____

_____

_____

_____

_____

_____

_____

_____

_____

_____

_____

_____

_____

_____

_____

_____

_____

_____

_____

Photo: © Oliver Simon | Dreamstime.com

_____
_____
_____
_____
_____
_____
_____
_____
_____
_____
_____
_____
_____
_____
_____
_____
_____
_____

Photo: © Robyn Charnley | Dreamstime.com

Photo: © Iuliia Stepashova | Dreamstime.com

_____

_____

_____

_____

_____

_____

_____

_____

_____

_____

_____

_____

_____

_____

_____

_____

_____

_____

_____

_____

_____

_____

_____

_____

_____

_____

_____

_____

_____

_____

_____

_____

_____

_____

_____

_____

_____

_____

_____

Photo: © Mark Jones | Wikimedia

Photo: © Photokvu | Dreamstime.com

_____

_____

_____

_____

_____

_____

_____

_____

_____

_____

_____

_____

_____

_____

_____

_____

_____

_____

_____

_____

Photo: © Sbukley | Dreamstime.com

Photo: © Robyn Charnley | Dreamstime.com

_____

_____

_____

_____

_____

_____

_____

_____

_____

_____

_____

_____

_____

_____

_____

_____

_____

_____

Photo: © Photokvu | Dreamstime.com

_____

_____

_____

_____

_____

_____

_____

_____

_____

_____

_____

_____

_____

_____

_____

_____

_____

_____

Photo: © Lorna Roberts | Dreamstime.com

_____

_____

_____

_____

_____

_____

_____

_____

_____

_____

_____

_____

_____

_____

_____

_____

Photo: © Wirestock | Dreamstime.com

Photo: © Paulmccabe1 | Dreamstime.com

Photo: Video screenshot

Photo: © Lorna Roberts | Dreamstime.com

Other Titles in the *My Book About* Series

More coming soon! See all titles:

WriteMyBookAbout.com

"Don't chase people. Be yourself, do your own thing and work hard. The right people – the ones who really belong in your life – will come to you. And stay."
~ *Will Smith*

"I often warn people: Somewhere along the way, someone is going to tell you, 'There is no "I" in team.' What you should tell them is, 'Maybe not. But there is an "I" in independence, individuality and integrity."
- George Carlin

"In a survey of 90-year-olds, when asked what they would have done differently, they responded, 'Risk more, reflect more and leave a legacy that matters.'"
- *Dr. Linda Livingstone*
Dean of Pepperdine University Business School

10 Seconds of Inspiration

Get images like these delivered to your inbox every Saturday morning. Enjoy and share!

Visit

CreateTeachInspire.com/ss

to join Shareable Saturday

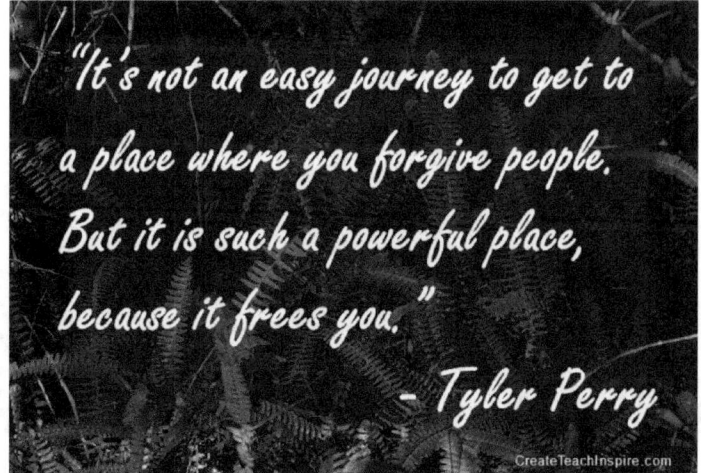

"You cannot get through a single day without having an impact on the world around you. What you do makes a difference, and you have to decide what kind of difference you want to make."

– Jane Goodall

CreateTeachInspire.com

"It's not an easy journey to get to a place where you forgive people. But it is such a powerful place, because it frees you."

– Tyler Perry

CreateTeachInspire.com

A great way to wrap up your week!

Visit **CreateTeachInspire.com/ss** to join Shareable Saturday